G000123761

Cover illustration. A Centurion Mk 12 breasts a ridge during driver training at the School of Electrical and Mechanical Engineers on Borden Heath. (Simon Dunstan)

British Battle Tanks

1945 TO THE PRESENT

SIMON DUNSTAN

ARMS AND ARMOUR PRESS

London – Melbourne – Harrisburg. Pa. – Cape Town

1. The Conqueror was powered by the M120 version of the Meteor, developing 810bhp by means of fuel injection which gave a top speed of 20mph. A Conqueror Mk 2 negotiates a knife edge at Bovington; the Mk 2 featured a fume extractor for the 120mm gun in place of the simple counterweight on the Mk 1. The turret stowage basket was a retrospective modification on production Mk 2s. (MOD)

Introduction

Tanks Illustrated 5: British Battle Tanks, 1945 to the Present
Published in 1983 by
Arms and Armour Press, Lionel Leventhal Limited,
2-6 Hampstead High Street, London NW3 1QQ;
4-12 Tattersalls Lane, Melbourne, Victoria 3000,
Australia; Sanso Centre, 8 Adderley Street,
PO Box 94, Cape Town 8000, South Africa;
Cameron and Kelker Streets, PO Box 1831,
Harrisburg, Pennsylvania 17105, USA.

British Library Cataloguing in Publication Data:
Dunstan, Simon
British battle tanks, 1945 to the present.—(Tanks
illustrated; 5)
1. Tanks (Military science)—Great Britain—
History
I. Title   II. Series
623.74′752′0941   UG446.5
ISBN 0-85368-602-5

Layout by Anthony A. Evans
Typesetting and make-up by
Wyvern Typesetting Limited, Bristol
Printed in Great Britain by
William Clowes (Beccles) Limited.

2. With its main armament at maximum elevation, this Chieftain of the Queen's Dragoon Guards is also equipped with Simfire. When the crew go through the firing sequence, the flash generator (above the searchlight housing) emits pyrotechnics to simulate the flash and smoke of gun fire, and the laser projector pulses. The detectors of the target tank pick up the laser pulses and a smoke pyrotechnic is ignited to indicate that the tank has been knocked out. (MOD)

During the Second World War, British tanks were generally inferior to their German opponents with respect to their firepower and armour protection, while their high mobility in the early years was severely compromised by chronic unreliability. Since the war British designers have consistently pursued a policy that would prevent British troops ever taking the field again with tanks of inferior armour and armament. Unlike the European school of thought which advocates high mobility and firepower to ensure survival on the battlefield, the British consider that firepower is the primary attribute of a tank in defeating enemy armour at long ranges, followed closely by heavy armour protection to enable it to absorb punishment and manoeuvre at close quarters with relative immunity in a theatre of high-intensity warfare. Immediately after the war Britain abandoned the misguided doctrine of dividing tanks into 'Cruiser' and 'Infantry' types and adopted the idea of a 'Universal' or 'general purpose' tank, later to be known as the 'Main Battle Tank' (MBT). The first of these was Centurion, an excellent design capable of being repeatedly upgraded. Originally armed with the 17pdr, it was subsequently fitted with the 20pdr and finally the 105mm gun; the frontal armour was increased and fuel capacity more than doubled. Its successor, Chieftain, was designed from the outset to mount the most powerful and effective gun feasible, with a range of ammunition capable of defeating different armour arrangements at considerable range. The latest British Main Battle Tank is Challenger. It incorporates the latest developments in tank technology, including advanced compound armour, a computerised fire control system and thermal-imaging equipment for night fighting. Challenger is the product of more than 60 years of British tank development and is one of the foremost AFV designs in the world. The photographs on the following pages form a representative cross-section of the principal battle tanks employed by the British Army in the past forty years. In preparing them for publication I wish to thank the public relations departments of the Ministry of Defence; HQ Royal Armoured Corps Centre; National Army Museum; James Haddon; Vickers Defence Systems; and Les Wiggs of *Soldier* Magazine.

▲3

▲4 ▼5

3. The first new tank to enter service with the British Army after the Second World War was the Centurion. Designed in the closing years of that conflict, six prototype vehicles were rushed to Germany in May 1945, but arrived too late to see action. The Centurion Mk 1 was armed with a 17pdr (76.2mm) gun with a Besa 7.92mm machine-gun on a uni-axial mounting in the mantlet as secondary armament, allowing the loader to fire at targets independently of the main gun. A total of 100 Mk 1s were built and the type first entered service in December 1946. (HQ RAC Centre)

4. A Comet of 2nd Infantry Division advances through a bomb-damaged German town during an exercise soon after the war. Essentially an up-gunned and up-armoured Cromwell, the A34 Comet was the last in the line of Cruiser tanks that had originated in 1936 from a design by the American J. Walter Christie. The Comet saw action in the final months of the war. (*Soldier*)

5. The first major production variant of Centurion was the Mk 2 with a fully-cast turret of superior ballistic protection and a coaxial Besa machine-gun. It also featured gun control equipment stabilised in both azimuth and elevation to allow accurate firing on the move. Centurion was the first tank with such a system and it has proved highly successful in service. (*Soldier*)

6. The Centurion Mk 2 retained the 17pdr main armament of its predecessor which incorporated a muzzle brake. The characteristic muzzle blast of this weapon, with propellant fumes venting to each side, is apparent as this Centurion of 8th Royal Tank Regiment fires at a target on the tank gunnery ranges, Warcop. (*Soldier*)

7. 'Alligator', a Comet Type B, advances in formation across typical rolling countryside of the North German plains. The Type B had twin armoured fishtail exhaust pipes in the rear hull plate in place of the Cromwell exhaust system of the Type A which vented through the top engine deck. (*Soldier*)

8. It was not until 1948 that Centurion was unveiled to the general public after major manoeuvres in Germany entitled Exercise 'Agility'. Here, a Centurion Mk 2 bearing the famous red jerboa of 7th Armoured Brigade (formerly Division) churns up a field during 'Agility'. Note the registration number T351863 on the turret side below the stowage bin; in 1948 the T-registration system for tanks was superseded by a civilian type of numbers/letters/numbers. (*Soldier*)

9. The crew of a Centurion Mk 3 abandon their tank after being 'knocked-out' by an attacking plane during Exercise 'Holdfast' in September 1952, the largest Allied manoeuvres in West Germany up to that time, when NATO armies and air forces of 'Blueland' conducted a holding action against 'superior enemy forces' from 'Greenland' – a scenario which has been repeated annually ever since. (*Soldier*)

▲8 ▼9

10. Although Centurion lacked the high road speed of its Cruiser predecessors (21mph as against 32mph for Cromwell), it had superior battlefield mobility as well as greater firepower and armour protection. A Centurion Mk 2 demonstrates its agility by negotiating a 20ft vertical drop during a display at Bovington in 1951. The strengthening ribs on the transmission covers and the muzzle brake of the 17pdr gun are the principle identifying features of the Mk 2. (*Soldier*)

11. A striking example of the problems of conducting tactical field exercises in the agricultural areas of Germany as sheep graze oblivious to the presence of two Centurions Mk 3. German farmers are totally familiar with the procedures of claiming compensation for damage incurred during manoeuvres intended to safeguard their homeland. (*Soldier*)

10▲ 11▼

12. Centurions Mk 3 of 7th
Armoured Brigade negotiate
a floating Bailey bridge
across the River Weser
during autumn manoeuvres
in 1950. The nearer
Centurions are equipped
with jettisonable fuel drums
(improvised at unit level in
Germany) to augment the
tanks' poor radius of action,
while the Centurion Mk 3 in
the background carries the
more complex auxiliary fuel
tank designed by FVRDE
(Fighting Vehicle Research
and Development
Establishment) – less
effective in the field because
it impeded turret traverse
and depression of the main
armament to the rear.
(*Soldier*)

13. During the early fifties
the Suez Canal Zone in
Egypt was an area of
continual tension and on
more than one occasion it
was necessary to use tanks to
restore civil order. At this
time Egypt and Libya were
major training areas of the
British Army for desert
warfare, dramatically
illustrated by this Centurion
Mk 3 advancing at speed in a
cloud of sand. (*Soldier*)

14. The Centurion first saw
combat during the Korean
War. The country was
uniformly hostile to
armoured warfare, with
innumerable steep hills
interspersed with rice
paddy-fields. In this
photograph Centurions of C
Squadron, 8KRIH, advance
along a typical unpaved
Korean road against a
backdrop of forbidding hills.
(*Soldier*)

▲12   ▼13

14▼

▲15 ▼16

15. Besides the three sabre squadrons equipped with Centurions, the 8th Hussars incorporated a Reconnaissance Troop of Cromwells, two of which can be seen to the left in this leaguer position. Several of the Cromwells were lost in the Battle of the Happy Valley in January 1951 when they and the Churchills of 7RTR covered the withdrawal of 29th Brigade to Seoul in the face of the massive Chinese invasion. (National Army Museum)

16. The Centurions of the 8th Hussars had been in Korea for three months before they fired a shot in anger. On 11 February 1951, while in support of an American infantry patrol along the Han River, two Centurions of C Squadron, 'Caughoo' and 'Colorado', engaged enemy positions and a tank concealed under a railway bridge at a range of 3,000 yards. The tank was quickly destroyed and was identified as a Cromwell captured by the Chinese in the Battle of the Happy Valley. Here, 'Colorado' fires 20pdr AP at the Cromwell during this action. (*Soldier*)

17. Once established on a ridge or hilltop the tanks were able to dominate the surrounding countryside with highly accurate gunfire. From these heights enemy positions were engaged and infantry attacks supported by tank fire. Two Centurions of 3 Troop, B Squadron, 8KRIH, negotiate a ridge as they seek enemy targets on the opposing hills. (National Army Museum)

18. The problems of mobility encountered in Korea are graphically illustrated as this Centurion Mk 3 claws its way up a precipitous hillside with flooded rice paddies in the valley below. The Centurion displayed outstanding agility in such terrain and there were few hills that defeated it provided a careful driving technique were adopted whereby the tank did not deviate from a straight line while in motion. To do so could result in track-shedding and total loss of control. (National Army Museum)

19. In the last two years of the Korean War the front lines were static. The tanks were emplaced in permanent positions on commanding hilltops with wide arcs of fire. Their tracks and suspension were protected by sandbags while ammunition supplies were dug into the hillside beside them. These positions were protected from infantry attack by wide belts of barbed wire and minefields. Because of the accuracy and firepower of the tanks, enemy movement was impossible during daylight without bringing down a fusillade of high explosive. At night the tanks provided covering fire for infantry patrols in no man's land and conducted defensive fire plans to counter enemy attacks. A Centurion Mk 3 of B Squadron, 1st Royal Tank Regiment, stands on the right hand half-troop position of Point 335, the highest hill on the front of 1st Commonwealth Division. (Private Collection)

▲19

20. A Comet Type B, with the name 'Gun Boat Annie' chalked on the turret stowage bin, pauses by the roadside during a field exercise in Germany. Below the fishtail exhausts are smoke dischargers and below those a towing bar for a 17pdr anti-tank gun. The Comet was soon replaced in Europe by the Centurion, but it also served in the Suez Canal Zone and Palestine during the immediate post-war years. (*Soldier*)

21. The principal production version of the Centurion was the Mk 3 and 2,833 were built between 1948 and 1956. By the early fifties initial operating problems had been resolved and the tank proved to be both reliable and effectual. Because of its success during the Korean War it attracted considerable overseas sales and has seen service with the armies of more than a dozen nations. (MOD)

20▲ 21▼

▲22

22. Advancing in a cloud of dust, a Centurion Mk 5/1 shows its paces during a public display at Bovington; the Centurion had a sustained cross-country speed of approximately 15mph. The suffix /1 indicates that the glacis plate has been up-armoured. The appliqué patch increased armour protection over the front to five inches (126mm). This modification was applied to the majority of Centurions in British service. (Simon Dunstan)

23. Before the widespread use of armoured personnel carriers, infantry were transported on the backs of tanks in much the same manner as the Soviet practice of 'desant'. Troops were trained to disembark from tanks moving at speeds of up to 10mph. One lesson that the soldiers quickly learned was not to stand on the exhaust covers as the heat could cause the soles of their boots to disintegrate. In this picture, men of the Royal Welsh Fusiliers leap from a Centurion Mk 5. The black and white stripes on the cooling air deflector are a convoy distance marker. (National Army Museum)

24. The Centurion was the British Army's principal MBT for more than twenty-five years; the success of the design lay in the finely-balanced combination of firepower, protection and mobility. (Simon Dunstan)

25. The Centurion has proved to be the most successful British tank in the post-war era. It remains in front-line service with several armies throughout the world. (Simon Dunstan)

▼23

26. A Centurion Mk 10 of 1st Royal Tank Regiment churns up the sand in the Western Aden Protectorate, 1966. (MOD)

27. Chieftain – the British Army's current MBT; it remains one of the most powerful AFVs in NATO. (MOD)

28. The nationalisation of the Suez Canal by Colonel Nasser in July 1956 precipitated an Anglo-French expedition to restore control of the international waterway. Ships of the Royal Navy approach the coast of Egypt at the outset of Operation 'Musketeer'; in the foreground is an LST (Landing Ship Tank) loaded with Centurions Mk 5 of C Squadron, 6th Royal Tank Regiment, which made an assault landing over the beaches of Port Said on 6 November 1956. (James Haddon)

29. In its role as armoured support to the Royal Marines of 40 and 42 Commandos in the assault, the Centurions of 6RTR were equipped for deep-wading. The kit comprised extensions to the exhaust pipes, trunking for the air inlet and outlets and, just behind the turret stowage bins, flexible rubber tubing for the breather holes of the fuel tanks. The white capital 'H' on the turret roof was carried by all vehicles and served as a mutual recognition sign to the Anglo/French forces. The 'H' signified Hamilcar, the original name for Operation 'Musketeer'. (James Haddon)

28▲   29▼

▲30 ▼31

30. The Centurion Mk 5 of Major John Joly, the commanding officer of C Squadron, 6RTR, halts on the streets of Port Said after the action in which 9 and 10 Troops led the advance into the town in support of Royal Marines mounted in LVTs. The marking on the left front trackguard is a shipping instruction and that on the right indicates the type of oils used in the tank. (James Haddon)

31. During the fighting on L-Day (6 November), Brigadier 'Tubby' Madoc, the commanding officer of the Royal Marines, approached the Italian Consulate where the Egyptian Military Governor was known to be sheltering. Finding the building barred and shuttered and receiving no response to his entreaties, Madoc ordered Captain Tim Green, the troop leader of 12 Troop, to smash down the front door with his tank. The Egyptian governor promptly agreed to discuss a ceasefire. The crew of Green's Centurion Mk 5 stand by during the negotiations prior to their forcible entry; around the turret ring and wheel nuts is the black 'Prestik' waterproofing compound which sealed the tank during wading operations. (James Haddon)

32. Tankpower gives way to horsepower as a Centurion Mk 5 patrols the streets of Port Said after the ceasefire. Across the glacis plate the tank is named RATTLE in black capital letters on a white rectangle; the tanks in this troop were named 'Shake', 'Rattle' and 'Roll'. On the lower hull front is the unit serial '59' in white on a red square and to the right, below the registration number, is the insignia of 3rd Division, three black triangles on a red circle. (James Haddon)

33. With the ceasefire in effect, a Centurion Mk 5 of 9 Troop stands guard on a road junction while troops search buildings for weapons. Note the black stripe around the turret displayed by all British and French tanks as a mutual recognition device. This was a necessary precaution as the Egyptians also had Centurions in service, but only Soviet SU100 tank destroyers were encountered in Port Said. The Anglo-French forces withdrew from Egypt in December. (James Haddon)

32▲ 33▼

▲34 ▼35

34. The commander of a Ferret Mk 2 confers with the loader of a Centurion Mk 5/1 during Exercise 'Storm King' in November 1964. On the glacis plate to the right of the spare tracklinks is the container for a hood to cover the driver's position in foul weather. The turret top and gun barrel are wrapped in scrim to camouflage the tank when in hull-down fire positions. (*Soldier*)

35. The Conqueror Heavy Gun Tank was developed to counter the Soviet IS–3 which was more powerfully armed and armoured than any Western tank. Weighing 65 tons, the Conqueror was armed with a 120mm gun firing APDS and HESH ammunition. Because of their size and weight the projectiles and cartridges were loaded separately and only 35 rounds were carried. The Conqueror entered service with the British Army in 1956. (MOD)

36. As an army of occupation in Germany during the immediate post-war years, British tanks carried live ammunition and had complete freedom of movement. An order to occupy a certain grid point was accomplished irrespective of whether it was a farm barn or a private garden although by creative map-reading such positions frequently turned out to be near beerhouses. Here, a Centurion Mk 5/1 takes up its allotted position in the corner of a garden, having ripped the cobblestones off the road. (*Soldier*)

37. Amphibious warfare has been an integral part of British Army doctrine for many years. In the days of a far-flung Empire, many overseas territories were protected by the Royal Navy with an Amphibious Warfare Squadron incorporating tank landing craft permanently loaded with tanks for rapid deployment in potential or actual troublespots. Here, a Centurion Mk 5, equipped with a deep-wading kit, motors ashore during a training exercise. (MOD)

38. In 1952, a mono-wheel fuel trailer was introduced to augment the inadequate range of the Centurion. It was attached to the tank by two trailing arms which embodied fuel lines to transfer petrol to the main fuel tanks. The fuel trailer could be discarded in an emergency by means of explosive charges. A Centurion Mk 5 of 5th Royal Tank Regiment tows its fuel trailer over muddy terrain showing the swivelling mono-wheel at the rear. (*Soldier*)

39. A Forward Repair Team undertake an engine change in the field with the aid of their Light Aid Detachment halftrack. A criticism of the Centurion was the lack of accessibility for maintenance and the undue length of time needed to replace major components such as the engine or gearbox. The time necessary to change the 650bhp Meteor engine was commonly in excess of 12 hours. (MOD)

40. The mono-wheel fuel trailer proved decidedly unpopular with tank crews; the increased length of the vehicle made manoeuvring more difficult and the trailing arms frequently broke or became distorted. One of the major problems was the danger of fire since it was possible to overfill the fuel tanks, spilling petrol into the engine compartment as was the case with this Centurion Mk 5 which is being recovered by a Centurion ARV Mk 2. (MOD)

▲41 ▼42

41. Comets of the 1st Royal Tank Regiment parade on the streets of Kowloon in Hong Kong to mark the Queen's birthday in 1958. The Comet remained in service with the British Army until 1959 and with the Territorial Army until well into the sixties. This photograph shows the principal post-war modifications: smoke dischargers on the turret sides, a blade vane sight forward of the commander's cupola, and the armour fillet welded to the glacis plate to protect the join with the vertical front plate. (MOD)

42. 'Track-bashing' – the bane of every tankman's life, but a vital necessity for the efficient running of any tank. Changing tracks was a long and arduous task and even more so after 'track-shedding' when, on occasions, the tracks became so jammed that it was only possible to remove them with the help of oxy-acetylene equipment or explosives. The interesting vehicle in the background is a Centurion Tower; a turretless gun tank employed as a recovery vehicle. (MOD)

43. Centurions Mk 11 and 12 conduct night firing exercises on the tank gunnery ranges at Hohne in Germany. Since the Second World War most battle tanks have been fitted with night-fighting equipment based on active infra-red projectors or, in recent years, passive observation devices. Visible above the path of the main armament projectile is the trace of the three spotting rounds fired by the .50in ranging gun. (MOD)

44. The closing of the Soviet sector in Berlin in August 1961 caused an international crisis. As part of the Berlin Independent Brigade Group, the tanks of C Squadron, 4th Royal Tank Regiment, acted as armoured support to the beleaguered garrison. 'Discoverer', a Centurion Mk 5, stands guard at Stakken on the border of East Germany; note the traditional 'Chinese Eye' insignia of 4RTR on the turret stowage bin. (MOD)

43▲   44▼

45. A Centurion Mk 8/1 of the Scots Greys wades ashore from a landing craft of the Amphibious Warfare Squadron in the Persian Gulf, 1963. By this time the cumbersome metal trunking of the previous deep-wading equipment had been replaced by a simpler PVC kit which allowed access for servicing and was capable of repeated use. (MOD)

46. The British Army employs tankdozers to perform minor engineering tasks on the battlefield such as digging hull-down fire positions or clearing rubble in urban areas. Tankdozers are issued on a scale of one per squadron. Here, a Centurion Mk 5 Tankdozer lies concealed in a fire position on the edge of a wood. Unlike standard gun tanks, Centurion tankdozers were not up-armoured on the glacis plate because the weight of extra armour and dozer blade overloaded the front suspension units. (MOD)

47. In addition to waging a bitter struggle in the streets of Aden, the Army guarded the protectorate against outside attack. Displaying on the infantry telephone box the emblem of the Aden garrison, a black dhow on a yellow square, a Centurion Mk 6 fires its main armament during gunnery training in the desert, 1964. (MOD)

48. To augment the heavy firepower of the L1 120mm gun, the Conqueror embodied a complex sighting and fire control system for greater accuracy at long ranges. It centred on the commander's fire control turret with independent power traverse and coincidence range-finder. Having assessed the range the commander could either fire the gun himself or hand over control to the gunner while he located another target. A Conqueror Mk 2 is refuelled from a Bedford RL petrol bowser during a field exercise in Germany, 1963. (MOD)

▲45　▼46

47▲ 48▼

49. With the advent of the L7 105mm gun, a .5in Browning was fitted in the Centurion's mantlet as a ranging gun to determine range data out to 1,500 metres. An additional aid to accuracy was the provision of a thermal jacket for the main armament as carried on this Centurion Mk 6/2 of the 13th/18th Hussars, the winning team during the Canada Cup NATO tank gunnery competition of 1966. (MOD)

50. 'Roker Park', a Centurion Mk 5/1 (LR) of the 5th Royal Inniskilling Dragoon Guards, speeds across country during a training exercise in Germany. The suffix LR denotes 'long-range' as the tank incorporates a 100-gallon

▲49

armoured fuel tank bolted to the rear hull plate in order to increase combat range which on early models of the Centurion was little more than a totally inadequate 30 miles cross-country. (MOD)

51. In 1961, the newly independent kingdom of Kuwait was threatened by invasion from Iraq. Responding to her treaty obligations the British Government promptly dispatched units of the Amphibious Warfare Squadron to the Persian Gulf in order to deter aggression. A Centurion Mk 8/1 of the 3rd Carabiniers lands on the beaches of Kuwait; the Mk 8 may be identified by the flat gun mantlet and the commander's split cupola hatch. (MOD)

52. Tension remained high in Kuwait for several weeks as the tanks of 3rd Carabiniers manoeuvred along the Moutla Ridge overlooking the frontier, the only possible route for Iraqi tanks, but this display of force averted a conflict which held the intriguing prospect of Centurion fighting Centurion as the Iraqis were also equipped with the tank. Here, tanks and infantry train in the blistering heat of the desert where temperatures rose as high as 140° Fahrenheit. (MOD)

53. Centurions Mk 6/2 of the Royal Hussars drive ashore from a MEXE float during an exercise in the Hong Kong New Territories, December 1972. The Centurion Mk 6/2 was an up-armoured and up-gunned Mk 5 incorporating a .50in ranging gun and thermal jacket for the 105mm gun. By this time Centurion had been replaced in the armoured regiments of BAOR by Chieftain, and Hong Kong was the last posting for the Centurion Main Battle Tank in the British Army. (MOD)

54. An impressive display by more than 300 AFVs of 20th Armoured Brigade, with lines of Centurions stretching to the horizon during a parade marking the conclusion of manoeuvres in 1965. In the foreground is the Brigade Artillery equipped with American M44 155mm Self-Propelled Howitzers and Centurions Mk 5 (LR) as gunner OP tanks. The M44 was superseded by the FV433 Abbot 105mm SP gun. (*Soldier*)

▼53

▲55 ▼56

55. In 1956, the Centurion was extensively redesigned to overcome the deficiencies of earlier models and to incorporate further improvements. The new vehicle was built by Leyland Motors and was designated Mk 7. The principal alteration was the enlarged rear hull, accommodating more fuel under armour and effectively doubling the tank's range. When up-armoured and re-gunned with the L7 105mm it became Mk 9, shown here with its modified rear end. (HQ RAC Centre)

56. The infra-red night-fighting equipment fitted to Centurion was manufactured by GEC from a basic design by Philips. It featured twin headlights on the glacis plate with IR filters on the outer lamps and a 21in IR projector mounted on the mantlet. The system had an effective range of approximately 1,000 yards for night firing and approximately 100 yards for night driving. A Centurion Mk 9/1 lies concealed in bracken with its IR equipment shown to advantage. (HQ RAC Centre)

57. A brace of Chieftains Mk 2 are hosed down after a day's training at Bovington. (Simon Dunstan)

58. Moving across the flat prairie of the BATUS training area in Canada, a Chieftain Mk 5 undergoes a battlegroup exercise in 1978. (MOD)

▲59 ▼60

59. A Chieftain Mk 9(C) of the 17th/21st Lancers conducts gunnery training on the ranges at Lulworth. (Simon Dunstan)

60. The first production Challenger Main Battle Tank was presented to the British Army on 16 March 1983. First conceived in 1975, the General Service Requirement for Challenger was issued in early 1979 and the design was accepted in December 1982. Production began immediately and Challenger entered regimental service with the Royal Hussars in Germany in October 1983 – a remarkably short development cycle for a modern weapon system. (MOD)

61. The final versions of Centurion, Mks 11, 12 and 13, featured the L7 105mm gun, thermal jacket, .5in Browning ranging gun, up-armoured glacis plate and infra-red night-fighting equipment. The Mk 11 was based on the Mk 5, the 12 on the 7 and the 13 on the 10. A number of specialised Centurion vehicles remain in service to this day and several gun tanks are retained for driver training, including this Mk 12 at the School of Electrical and Mechanical Engineers in Borden. (Simon Dunstan)

62. A Centurion Mk 5 leads the way over rough terrain on Bovington Heath followed by its successor Chieftain. The Centurion served as the principal main battle tank of the British Army for more than twenty-five years. It proved to be reliable and highly effectual in combat. It remains in front-line service with several armies throughout the world and is still a formidable fighting machine. (HQ RAC Centre)

63. On 22 July 1974 the last Centurion MBT was officially withdrawn from service with the Royal Armoured Corps. In a ceremony to mark the event, Centurion Mk 13 04CC87 fired a final salute on the gunnery ranges at Lulworth. It was crewed by four distinguished members of the RAC with more than a century of service to the Crown between them. Acting as commander was Colonel Eric Offord, with Major Bert Starr as gunner, Lieutenant-Colonel Ken Hill as loader and Major Frank Mitchell as driver. (Simon Dunstan)

61▲

62▲   63▼

▲64 ▼65

64. 65 tons of Conqueror
Mk 2 smash through the
trees on a tank training
ground in Germany, 1964.
Up to nine Conquerors were
issued to most armoured
regiments in BAOR. They
were either formed into
troops of three, one to each
Centurion squadron, or else
became the fourth tank in a
standard troop. The basic
role of the Conqueror was
the destruction of tanks at
ranges beyond the capability
of Centurion. (MOD)

65. The massive bulk of the
Conqueror and its powerful
120mm gun can be clearly
seen in this photograph of a
Mk 2 in Germany, 1964.
The Mk 2 had a revised
glacis plate and a single
periscope for the driver in
place of the three on the
Mk 1. Because of its great
weight, high servicing loads
and the arrival of the highly
effective L7 105mm gun for
Centurion, the Conqueror
was withdrawn from service
in 1966. (MOD)

66. The Chieftain Main
Battle Tank was unveiled in
September 1962 during a
display at the Fighting
Vehicles Research and
Development Establishment
(FVRDE), Chertsey. In this
photograph a prototype
Chieftain with its turret front
and glacis plate masked for
security purposes crosses a
No. 6 Tank Bridge. (*Soldier*)

67. The Chieftain Mk 2
entered service with the
British Army in November
1966. The first unit to be
issued with the tank was the
11th Hussars. The original
production model, the Mk 1,
was used solely as a training
vehicle from 1963 and only
40 were built. Here, a
Chieftain Mk 2, negotiates a
water dip. (Simon Dunstan)

68. The L60 engine of an
early production Chieftain is
removed by an FV434
maintenance vehicle.
Originally designed to meet a
NATO requirement for
multi-fuel capability, which
added to its complexity, the
Leyland L60 has proved
unsatisfactory in service with
limited power output and
poor reliability. Early engine
models developed less than
600bhp and attempts to
increase output resulted in
reduced reliability. After
many years of development
both aspects have been
improved significantly.
(MOD)

66▲

67▲   68▼

69. Churning over the dust bowl at Fallingbostell in Germany, a Chieftain Mk 2 of 3rd Royal Tank Regiment displays the great length of its main armament. The 19 feet of gun is shrouded with a thermal jacket to minimise barrel bend resulting from differential cooling by crosswinds or rain. The thermal jacket enhances accuracy at long ranges when factors such as barrel bend become increasingly significant. (MOD)

70. The principal attribute of Chieftain is its powerful L11 120mm gun which is capable of destroying hostile tanks at ranges in excess of 3,000 metres. It fires APDS, HESH, Smoke and Illuminating rounds. The ammunition is separated into charge and projectile for ease of handling and stowage, with the combustible bagged charges stored in water jackets as protection against ammunition fires. In this photograph a Chieftain Mk 2 of the Queen's Own Hussars moves across country. (MOD)

71. A Chieftain Mk 5 leads a column of FV432 Armoured Personnel Carriers over M2 Bridges across the River Weser in Germany, October 1972. The Mk 5 incorporates an uprated L60 engine of 720bhp giving a power-to-weight ratio of 13.3bhp per ton which, despite being the lowest among contemporary main battle tanks, still provides Chieftain with adequate tactical mobility. (*Soldier*)

72. It is virtually impossible to differentiate between the various Marks and sub-Marks of Chieftain since the majority of modifications and improvements are internal. The Mk 2 is one of the few Chieftain models that is readily identifiable, thanks to the twin water jerrycans on the turret side. In this photograph a Chieftain Mk 2 of 5th Royal Inniskilling Dragoon Guards takes up position on the Soltau training ground in Germany, 1974. (MOD)

▲69　▼70

73. Mounting a flash discharger above its 120mm gun to simulate main armament firing during field exercises, a Chieftain moves along a German forest track during Exercise 'Red Rat 74'. Threaded through the lifting handles of the bazooka plates is a wire to which foliage can be attached to provide camouflage. (MOD)

74. All British AFVs are fitted with smoke dischargers which create an instant smokescreen when moving in tactical bounds or when surprised by anti-tank weapons. These are mounted on the turret sides of Chieftain as on this Mk 3 which also has a splash board between the headlights. This was a later addition to Chieftain and it prevents tree limbs and débris from riding up the glacis plate into the driver's face. (MOD)

75. A Chieftain negotiates a No. 6 Tank Bridge laid by the Centurion Bridgelayer in the background during an exercise in Germany in 1974. The tank is fitted with Simfire equipment which adds considerably to the realism of tactical exercises by simulating the firing of the main armament and the effect of tank casualties. Above the 120mm gun the Simfire laser projector can be clearly seen. Laser detectors are positioned at each corner of the turret. (MOD)

▲76 ▼77

76. Well camouflaged with scrim netting and natural foliage, a Chieftain of the Queen's Own Hussars lies concealed in a hull-down fire position. It is from such emplacements, where only the thickest armour of turret front and glacis plate is exposed, that NATO tanks would attempt to blunt the armoured assaults of a Soviet aggressor. (MOD)

77. A rear view of a Chieftain Mk 2 reveals the two exhaust outlets of the Leyland L60 engine and the smaller exhaust outlet above of the Coventry Climax H30 auxiliary engine. The Chieftain is amply provided with external stowage boxes, enabling the fighting compartment to be kept as uncluttered as possible for maximum crew efficiency. Note the early-style gun crutch and spare tracklinks mounted at the rear. (MOD)

78. A Chieftain advances over a ploughed field beneath the imposing Schloss Marienberg during exercises in the autumn of 1976. When playing the role of enemy tanks during field exercises, the bazooka plates of Chieftains are removed to alter their appearance. On the left hand side of the turret is the Light Projector No. 2 Mk 3 which is a combined Xenon white light/infra-red searchlight for night fighting. (MOD)

79. The .50in Browning ranging gun is clearly visible on this Chieftain Mk 3/3 (XY) of the Queen's Royal Irish Hussars during calibration firing on a range in Germany. The suffix (XY) denotes that the tank has undergone various stages of the 'Totem Pole' and 'Sundance' programmes to improve engine reliability. It can be appreciated that the many modifications and improvements applied to Chieftain make for numerous different versions of the basic Marks. The Mk 3/3 incorporates many detailed improvements as well as the installation of a laser range-finder. (Simon Dunstan)

78▲ 79▼

45

80. A Chieftain Mk 6(C) with white crosses denoting enemy forces advances to contact during Exercise 'Avon Express' on Salisbury Plain. The Mk 6 is a Mk 2 brought up to Mk 5 automotive standard and employing improved ammunition for the ranging gun which is effective out to 2,500 metres instead of 1,800 metres. The suffix (C) denotes that Clansman radio equipment is installed. (MOD)

81. The fire control system of Chieftain incorporates a Browning .50in ranging gun coaxial to the main armament to enable the gunner to determine the range and azimuth bearing before he engages a target with an armour defeating round. Not only does it measure range, but it also takes account of air density, wind and trunnion tilt. It is ballistically matched to the 120mm HESH ammunition. On this Chieftain Mk 5 of the Royal Scots Dragoon Guards on manoeuvres in Germany, the 7.62mm L8A1 co-axial machine-gun is clearly visible above the main armament. (MOD)

82. 'Dikler', a Chieftain of 4th Royal Tank Regiment, advances across country. All the tanks of 4RTR have names beginning with the fourth letter of the alphabet. The difficulty in identifying the Mark numbers of Chieftain is compounded by the fact that earlier Marks have been modified to an automotive and fire control equipment standard of the Mk 5. Note the Combat Vehicle 'Dan Dare' helmets of the turret crew. (MOD)

83. A Chieftain Mk 5 of 4th/7th Royal Dragoon Guards traverses a No. 9 Tank Bridge during an autumn exercise in Germany, 1977. Chieftain is now fitted with a laser range-finder designated Tank Laser Sight No. 1 Mk 2 (TLS), highly accurate to a range of 10,000 metres. The installation of the TLS renders the ranging gun redundant and its removal provides more space inside the turret. (MOD)

84. Thundering across the Canadian prairie, a Chieftain Mk 5(C) of 5th Royal Inniskilling Dragoon Guards participates in a battlegroup exercise at the British Army Training Unit Suffield (BATUS), 1978. This front view shows the compact configuration of the hull and the well-sloped surfaces of the frontal armour which gives Chieftain a greater degree of protection than any of its contemporaries. (MOD)

85. The 7.62mm L37A1 machine-gun mounted on the commander's cupola is loaded with live ammunition by a member of the 5th Skins. The gun can be aimed and fired by remote control from within the turret and has an elevation of 90°, so providing a measure of anti-aircraft capability. The dual purpose (white/IR) spotlight is directly linked to the machine-gun. Note the wash/wiper unit mounted forward of each periscope. (MOD)

▲86   ▼87

86. A number of interesting features of the Chieftain are visible on this Mk 5(C), including its later style gun crutch, the armoured cowl of the gunner's periscope (to allow the changing of battle-damaged optics or 'swap-sights' under full armour protection), the armoured searchlight housing and the spare cooling fan drive belt draped around the smoke grenade discharger (an item with a high failure rate on earlier models of the L60). The turret can be traversed through 360° in 16 seconds. (MOD)

87. Their black berets and tanksuits enable us to identify the crews of the Royal Tank Regiment, seen here while their commander speaks to an infantryman via the tank/infantry telephone attached to the rear hullplate. Chieftains Mk 5(C) take part in tank/infantry co-operation exercises on Salisbury Plain during August 1978. Tanks fitted with Clansman radios, hence the suffix (C), can be identified by the characteristic box of the aerial tuning unit, visible here behind the left hand

smoke grenade discharger with an aerial mounted above. (MOD)

88. Displaying its callsign number 'Four-two Bravo' to the front, sides and rear, a Chieftain of the Life Guards moves through a German village in Lower Saxony during 'Spearpoint 80'. A can of lubricating oil is strapped to the rear stowage bin and a fanbelt is draped around the smoke grenade discharger for repairs in the field. (MOD)

89. At least one Chieftain in each tank squadron is fitted with a dozer blade appliqué kit designed by Automotive Products Ltd. The electro-hydraulically operated dozer blade can be mounted on any production version of Chieftain and the equipment is used for digging fire positions, clearing roads, preparing river crossing points and filling defiles or anti-tank ditches. This Chieftain Mk 5 of the 17th/21st Lancers has its dozer blade raised in its travelling configuration. (Simon Dunstan)

▲90 ▼91

90. The tank commander of a Chieftain Mk 5(C) observes advancing FV432 Armoured Personnel Carriers through binoculars as a Gazelle helicopter flies low over the rolling terrain at BATUS. At the rear of the turret is the No. 6 Mk 2 NBC pack which protects the crew from contaminating agents without the need to use respirators inside the turret. When closed-down, crews can maintain their full effectiveness for up to 48 hours. (MOD)

91. The crew of a Chieftain Mk 5(C) of 5th Royal Inniskilling Dragoon Guards set up a bivouac at the end of a day's training at Suffield. The engine decks are open for essential maintenance with the radiators in a vertical position to clear the cores of dust and débris which can cause overheating. (MOD)

▲92 ▼93

92. Chieftains of the Life Guards pause during 'Spearpoint 80', the field training exercise forming the culmination of 'Crusader 80' – the largest British Army manoeuvres since the formation of NATO. During tactical exercises most tanks are camouflaged with scrim netting which effectively breaks up the lines of turret front and main armament. (MOD)

93. A dramatic view of Chieftains of the Life Guards as they advance through the morning mist during the typically foul weather of Exercise 'Spearpoint 80'. (MOD)

94. Throughout its career, Chieftain has been progressively improved but, with the cancellation of its planned successor, MBT80, it has become necessary to institute further improvements. This is being achieved by the Chieftain Improvement Programme (CHIP) which will allow Chieftain to continue in front-line service throughout the 1990s. The principal improvements are the Improved Fire Control System (IFCS) and an Armour Piercing Fin Stabilised Discarding Sabot round which, taken together, greatly increase firepower. (MOD)

▲95 ▼96

95. Chieftains fitted with IFCS are recognisable by the mirror of the Muzzle Reference System (MRS) mounted on the end of the gun barrel. This device enables the gunner to align his sights with the gun barrel bore rapidly and precisely – a factor of great importance for accuracy at long ranges. The fitting of IFCS alters the basic Mark numbers of Chieftain – Mk 2 becomes Mk 9, Mk 3 to Mk 10, Mk 3/3 to Mk 11, and Mk 5 to Mk 12. (MOD)

96. A further major aspect of CHIP is the introduction of passive night-vision equipment. The active infra-red system and white-light searchlight is being replaced by thermal-imaging equipment with the ability to see in the dark, through battlefield smoke and in rain and mist. The equipment, which has been developed for Challenger, is known as TOGS (Thermal Observation and Gun Sighting System). (MOD)

97. In the late 1950s, Vickers developed a medium-weight tank of high mobility and firepower with lighter armour, following European design philosophy, for the export market. The 38-ton Vickers Mk 1 was adopted by the Indian Army under the name Vijayanta (Conqueror) in 1961. More than 1,000 Vijayantas have been built and they performed successfully during the Indo/Pakistan War of 1971. Powered by a de-rated version of the Chieftain's L60 engine and armed with the proven L7 105mm gun, the Vickers Mk 1 was purchased by Kuwait between 1970 and 1972 and took part in the October War of 1973 in defence of Damascus although it did not see action. (Vickers Defence Systems)

▲97   ▼98

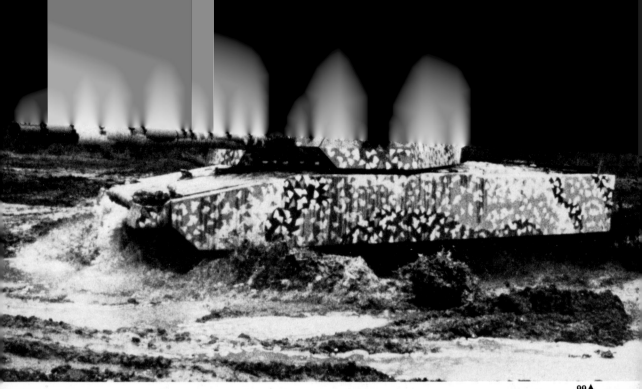

98. During the early 1970s, Vickers introduced an improved version of their MBT designated Mk 3. This model features a more heavily armoured cast turret offering superior ballistic protection, a more powerful L60 engine of 650bhp and a laser range-finder coupled to advanced image-intensification night-sights. The tank was later fitted with a General Motors 720bhp diesel engine to become the Mk 3B and this model has been purchased by the armies of Kenya and Nigeria. The Mk 3 is armed with the L7 105mm gun and weighs only 38 tons, making it highly suitable for countries where the terrain and rail networks demand a compact and easily transportable vehicle. It has the added virtue of being simpler to operate than the latest generation of MBTs designed for high-intensity warfare in Europe. (Vickers Defence Systems)
99. The latest Vickers tank is an entirely new design incorporating Chobham armour and many features of advanced technology. Weighing 43.6 tons, the Vickers Valiant has a level of protection, firepower and mobility as great as the latest

MBTs such as the Soviet T72. Its modest weight makes Valiant particularly attractive to countries where tactical considerations require an MBT of maximum firepower in the lightest possible hull configuration. (Vickers Defence Systems)
100. Valiant is a versatile weapons system capable of incorporating the specific needs of individual customers. To this end the 'Universal Turret' accepts either the L7 105mm gun, the current Chieftain L11 120mm gun or the Rheinmetall smooth-bore 120mm as fitted to Leopard 2. A variety of powerpacks up to 1,000bhp are available, such as the Rolls-Royce Condor, the General Motors 12V71T or the German MTU872 diesel engines. This Valiant is armed with the L11A5 120mm rifled gun. (Vickers Defence Systems)

▲101　▼102

101. Originally designed to meet a requirement of the Imperial Iranian Army for a Chieftain model of greater power and mobility, the FV4030/2 incorporates a Rolls-Royce 1,200hp engine and improved suspension. After the overthrow of the Shah, the sales contract was cancelled by the Khomeini regime. After further improvements to the design, the tank was purchased by Jordan under the name 'Khalid'. (MOD)

102. The distinctive lines of Khalid show the enlarged rear hull which accommodates the 1,200hp Condor powerpack. Khalid incorporates a Barr and Stroud Tank Laser Sight and the Marconi Space and Defence Systems Improved Fire Control System (IFCS). The Jordanian Army has a requirement for 278 Khalids. (MOD)

103. The Royal Ordnance Factory, Leeds, has produced a version of the basic Chieftain incorporating significant improvements in mobility and protection as well as an advanced fire control system. It is known as Chieftain '900' after the horsepower output of its de-rated Rolls-Royce Condor engine, and embodies Chobham armour for maximum protection. Intended for export to operators not wishing to deploy a tank as complex as Challenger, Abrams or Leopard 2, Chieftain 900 is a flexible design capable of being configured to individual customer requirements. (Simon Dunstan)

▲104 ▼105

104. This view of a Challenger prototype shows the configuration of Chobham armour over the frontal aspect which provides significantly greater protection against both kinetic and chemical energy attack than conventional armour. In accordance with long-standing design philosophy, greater emphasis is placed on frontal protection covering a 60° arc over turret and hull front. (Simon Dunstan)

105. Challenger entered service with the British Army in mid-1983, the first regiment to be equipped with the tank being the Royal Hussars. 264 Challengers are currently on order and it is planned to deploy them in one armoured division of 1st British Corps in BAOR. (MOD)

106. The FV4030 series of main battle tanks has been developed in an evolutionary manner from Chieftain and incorporates numerous advances in tank design, the most significant being the development of a revolutionary new form of protection for AFVs known as 'Chobham armour' after the town in Surrey near the Military Vehicles and Engineering Establishment (MVEE) where the armour was invented. The first application of Chobham armour was on an improved version of FV4030/2 called Shir 2 for the Iranian Army. After the repudiation of the Iranian tank contract, the FV4030/3 was further developed into the latest MBT for the British Army – Challenger. (MOD)

▲107 ▼108

107. The firepower of Challenger is centred on the L11A5 120mm rifled gun, identifiable by the narrower fume extractor than that on earlier models and the MRS at the barrel end. The 120mm APFSDS projectile will be the principal armour-piercing round for Challenger, capable of penetrating the frontal armour of T64 and T72 to beyond 2,000 metres range. (MOD)

108. IFCS allows Challenger to fire accurately on the move against stationary and moving targets. Both the commander and gunner can fire the main armament. Secondary armament is a coaxial L8A2 7.62mm machine-gun and an L37A2 7.62mm MG at the commander's cupola. Challenger carries 48 to 52 main armament rounds, depending on the mix of types stowed, and 4,000 rounds of 7.62mm ammunition. The stowage baskets on the turret front of this Challenger prototype are for camouflage nets. (Simon Dunstan)

109. The hull and turret of Challenger incorporate Chobham armour which provides high protection against both kinetic energy and chemical energy attack. A high level of immunity from the growing threat of anti-tank mines has been achieved by heavy belly armour and by sloping the hull sides. In addition, the external suspension units facilitate battlefield repair following mine attack. (MOD)

110. Challenger – the British Army's latest Main Battle Tank, the culmination of sixty years of British tank development. (MOD)

109▲ 110▼

65

111. This top view of a production Challenger shows the lay-out of the Chobham-armoured turret and hull which gives the highest level of protection on any MBT. The armour can withstand multiple shots from the complete inventory of current Soviet anti-tank weapons. The armour protection is the heaviest of any MBT currently in service and is reflected in the tank's battle weight of 62 tons. (MOD)

▲112

112. The principal differences between the prototype and production Challenger are the narrower turret to conform with European railway loading gauges and the barbette on the turret side which houses a thermal imaging sensor for observation and gunnery at night and in poor weather. (MOD)

113. The 26-litre V-12 water-cooled Rolls-Royce diesel engine

and infinitely variable transmission combined with the highly effective Laser Engineering Hydrogas suspension provide Challenger with a high degree of tactical mobility and a cross-country speed twice that of Chieftain. The Challenger is capable of 56kph on the road. (MOD)

▼113